CHRISTMAS

By Donna Cocking

Published by Prim-Ed Publishing

Foreword

This thematic package, based on *'Christmas'*, has been designed for lower primary school students.

The activities have been organised into subject foci.

Thematic programming ideas have been included so that teachers may integrate the theme across the curriculum.

Contents

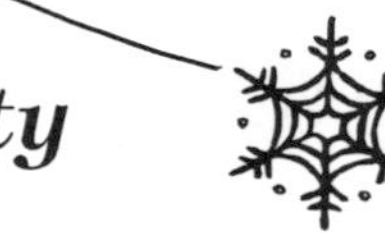

Investigation

Special Days
* Christmas Eve
* Christmas Day
* Christmas Night
* Boxing Day

History
* Yule log
* St Nicholas
* Epiphany
* Christmas feast

Significant figures
* Jesus Christ
* Mary
* Joseph
* Wise men

Customs

Food
* pudding
* cake
* turkey * ham
* mince pies

Decorations
* trees * ivy
* candles * holly
* lights * mistletoe
* stockings

Religious
* ceremonies
* carol singing
* festivals

Gifts
* cards
* wreaths
* bonbons

Nativity

Scene
* stable * manger
* inn * shepherds
* animals
* starry night

Art activities

* card making
* wrapping paper
* presents
* decorations
* model making

Class activities

* Christmas tree
* wall murals
* Christmas dinner
* concert

Christmas in different countries

Songs
* O Tannenbaum
* Six White Boomers
* Twelve Days of Christmas

Greetings
* Buon Natale
* Joyeux Noél
* Glad Jul

Toys

Find toys from the sleuths below and put them under the correct heading.
C W G S O L D I E R B T
A D U R A C Q U E T I R
R Q I G O L F C L U B U
D N T S C R A B B L E C
S V A Y O Y O Z Y Z A K
Z O R G A N N T V Q R Q
Toys with legs
N P Q B I C Y C L E Q T
D R U V H O R S E C A R
B A S K E T B A L L K A
A M T R A C T O R U D I
T W V Z T R U M P E T N
F I S H I N G R O D R V
Musical toys
Toys with wheels
Toys for sport or games

Add 'ing' to these words.

flash *flashing* ______ stock ______ ring ______

sing ______ eat ______ play ______

hang ______ sleep ______ roast ______

Use some of these 'ing' words to complete the sentence.

The turkey is r______.

The choir is s______.

The stockings are h______.

The bells are r______.

Unjumble

iinnggr

______

eenlpsgi

______

hafglisn

______

Write your own 'ing' words below.

The snow is ______ .

The candles are ______ .

The lights are ______ .

The stars are ______ .

Match these 'Christmas' pairs.

pine	paper	Merry	Eve
wrapping	tree	Santa	Night
coloured	pudding	Silent	Christmas
plum	lights	Christmas	Claus

Christmas is...

Use these words to complete this poem.

carol, mince pies, Santa, holly, card, candle, ham, merry,
angel, star, ice, reindeer, advent, Mary, stocking,
shepherds, turkey, mistletoe, snow, chimney,
church, toys, string, happy, ivy, music, stable,
Rudolph, incense, manger, tree

C ______________________________

H ______________________________

R ______________________________

I ______________________________

S ______________________________

T ______________________________

M ______________________________

A ______________________________

S ______________________________

Ch - Christmas!

Add 'ch' and draw four of these words.

___ ___ ristmas

s ___ ___ ool

___ ___ emist

a ___ ___ e

___ ___ risten

___ ___ oir

or ___ ___ estra

___ ___ orus

or ___ ___ id

List the words under the correct sound.

chicken, Christmas, cheer, children, chorus, orchestra

'ch'	'ch'
choir	church
____________	____________
____________	____________
____________	____________

Write the word for each meaning.

A group of singers ____________________

An unusual, colourful flower ____________________

Part of a song ____________________

A dull pain ____________________

A group of musicians ____________________

A group of fish ____________________

A December celebration ____________________

Blow the Trumpet!

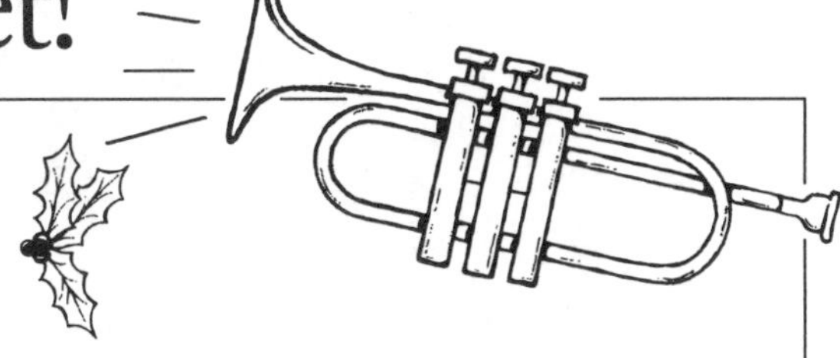

bright come clear drum
night cheer

Use the words above to complete this song.

Blow the trumpet, beat the drum.

Let the world know what will come.

Sing with voices loud and clear,

Let the world know Christmas is here.

Clang the cymbals, beat the drum.

Let the world know what will come.

Watch the candles burning ____________________.

See the shiny stars at ____________________.

Play the piano, beat the ____________________.

Let the world know what will ____________________.

Hear the church bells ringing ____________________,

Spread goodwill and Christmas ____________________.

Complete the last verse to finish the song.

Bang the tambourine, beat the drum.

Let the world know what will come.

____

____

Chant this song and perform the actions.
Use percussion instruments to accompany the chant.

A Letter to Santa

Fill in the missing words to complete the letter to Santa.

From ______________________________

____

To: Santa Claus
c/- The North Pole
At the Top of the World

Dear Santa,

How are you this Christmas? Could you please bring me one of these gifts this Christmas? For Christmas, I would like,

real two wooden

1. A __________ cricket bat with __________ sets of wickets and a __________ leather ball.

bright furry

2. A __________ teddy bear with a __________ ribbon around its neck.

glowing loud steam

3. A __________ train with a __________ night light and a __________ whistle.

red long blue

4. A __________ fishing rod with a __________ and __________ reel.

striped shiny flashing

5. A __________ bicycle with a __________ seat and two __________ lights.

Thank you, happy Christmas, from ______________________.

Construct a Santa Claus

Colour, cut and paste these shapes to make this Santa Claus puppet.

In the Toyshop

How much would it cost to buy:

(a) a toy bear and a bride doll? *20p + 50p = 70p*

(b) two toy bears and a cricket ball? ____________________

(c) a cricket bat and a bride doll? ____________________

(d) one beach ball and one cricket ball? ____________________

(e) three cricket balls? ____________________

(f) two bride dolls and a doll's pram? ____________________

Dot-to-Dot

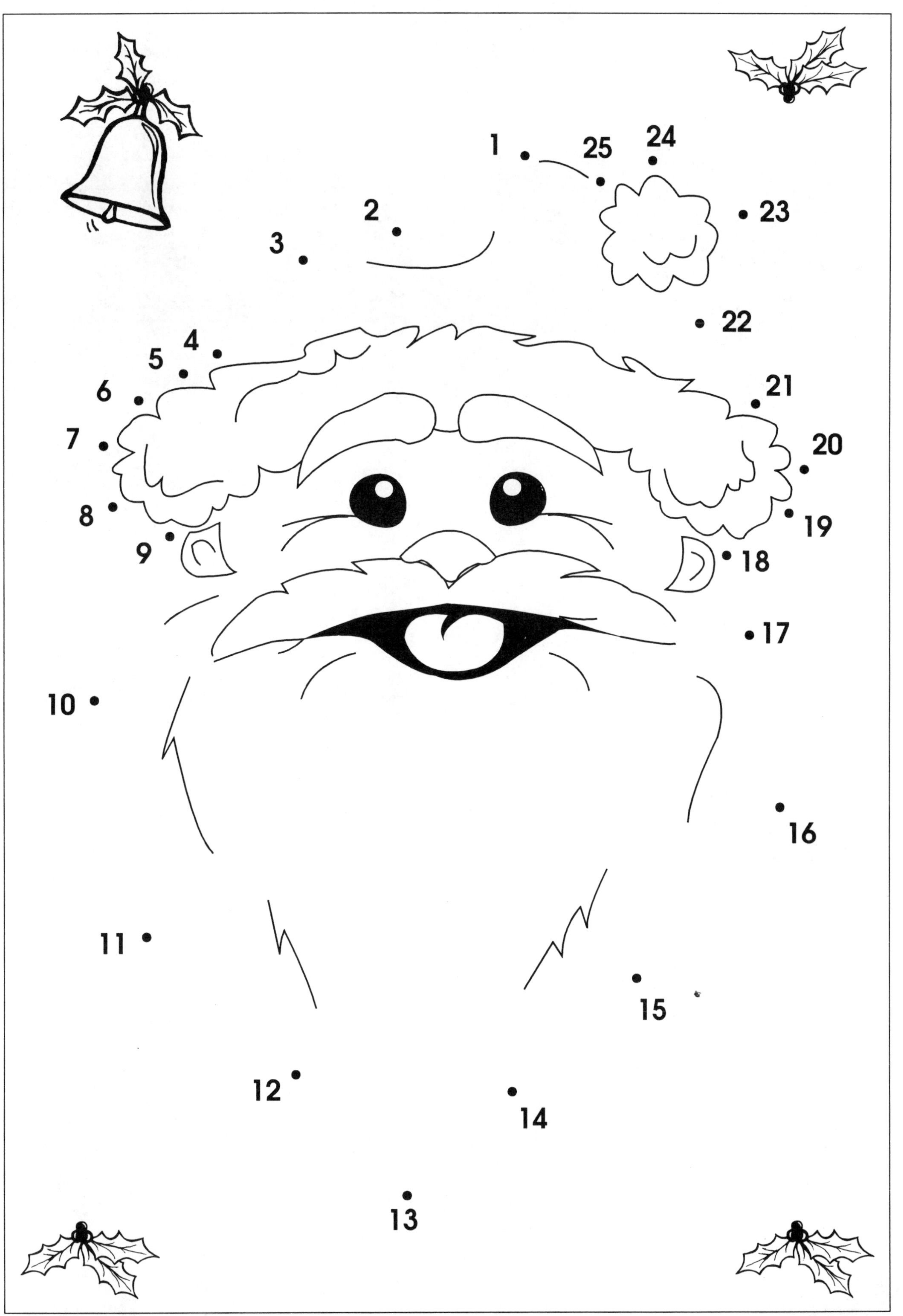

Race

Race a partner to the North Pole.

You will need:

- a die
- two markers

24	25	*End of Race*	
23 **lost your sled** (go back 3)	22	21	20
16	17	18	19 **You fell down** (go back 3)
15	14 **You're bogged** (throw 2 to move)	13	12
8	9	10	11
7	6 **Climb this hill** (go forward 4)	5	4 **Snow Storm** (miss a turn)
Start Racing	1	2	3

Mail Order Books

Choose three books from this range.

A Crafty Christmas
by Mary Bead

A Crafty Christmas £3.00

Create wonderful gifts and decorations. Easy-to-follow fun ideas. Includes templates for tree ornaments and wreath decorations.

The Christmas Cookbook £2.00

Christmas favourites and traditional recipes with colourful illustrations and easy step-by-step instructions.

The Christmas Cookbook
by Gwen Plum

ALL I WANT FOR CHRISTMAS
BY LISA ANGEL

All I Want for Christmas £3.00

A beautiful story about a Christmas wish that comes true.

Christmas Day £2.50

A fun book filled with poems and rhymes about Christmas.

Christmas Day
by Nicholas Saint

Complete the order form below.

Name: ______________________________

Address: ______________________________

______________ Postcode: __________ Telephone: ______________

Book title	Author	Quantity	Price
1. ______________	1. ______________		
______________	______________		
2. ______________	2. ______________		
______________	______________		
3. ______________	3. ______________		
______________	______________		

Advent Calendar

Complete this advent calendar.

Sunday		Tuesday			Friday	
31 New Year's Eve					1	Write 2 present list and cards
3 Concert practice		Post Christmas cards	6	John's birthday	8	
Grandma's house		12				16 Buy presents
	Class party			School concert	22 Decorate tree	Carol singing
Christmas Eve	**Christmas Day**	26 Boxing Day family party			29	

On what day is Christmas Day? ______________________

How many weeks before Christmas will the cards be posted? ______________________

On what day is the school concert? ______________________

How many days before Christmas Day will the presents be bought? ______________________

What is happening on Thursday, 7 December? ______________________

What event is happening on Boxing Day?

____

When is the class party? ______________________

In Santa's Workshop

In Santa's workshop the elves are very busy. Use the clues below to find out what each elf makes.

- The Green Elf can't sew.
- The Red Elf glues wheels.
- The Yellow Elf cuts out.
- The teddies and rabbits are filled with cotton wool.
- The Orange Elf is allergic to cotton wool.
- The Blue Elf is sewing a vest.
- The Yellow Elf sews a tail.
- The Brown Elf sews lace flowers.
- The Green Elf threads beads.
- The Orange Elf packs the tracks.

ELVES	Trains	Teddies	Necklaces	Bride Dolls	Rabbits	Cars
RED ELF						
YELLOW ELF						
GREEN ELF		X				
ORANGE ELF						
BLUE ELF						
BROWN ELF						

Complete

The Blue Elf makes ______________________.

The Red Elf makes ______________________.

The Green Elf makes ______________________.

The Brown Elf makes ______________________.

Colour this elf.

Instructions on page 28 teacher resource

Burning Candles

Draw and describe the shape and size of each candle.

1. ______________________

____

2. ______________________

____

3. ______________________

____

Complete

Candle 1 is as high as a ______________________.

Candle 2 is as small as a ______________________.

Candle 3 is as wide as a ______________________.

Your teacher will now light each candle. Watch them burn.

What colours are in the flames?

____

What sounds do the candles make?

____

What happens if you blow the flame gently?

____

Which candle burns the fastest?

____

Which candle burns the slowest?

____

What happens to candle 2?

____

Christmas Recipe

White Christmas

You will need:

2 cups Crispies
1 cup coconut
1 cup powdered milk
250 g butter
1 cup icing sugar
assorted dried fruits, glacé cherries, walnuts

1. Grease and line a square tin.
2. Roughly chop cherries, walnuts and dried fruits.
3. Mix all dry ingredients in a large bowl.
4. Melt butter in a saucepan and pour into bowl.
5. Stir until all ingredients are mixed.
6. Flatten mixture into tin and refrigerate until set.

Variations:

- Snowballs - roll into balls and toss in coconut.
- Choc Cups - add 1 cup cocoa and 275 g butter. Spoon into patty pans and ice with cooking chocolate.

Answer these questions.

How many cups of Crispies were used?

____

What did you chop into smaller pieces?

____

When was the butter added?

____

How long did it take for the mixture to set?

____

Draw and name four ingredients used.

Christmas Border

Paper Fun

Follow these directions to make Christmas paper decorations.

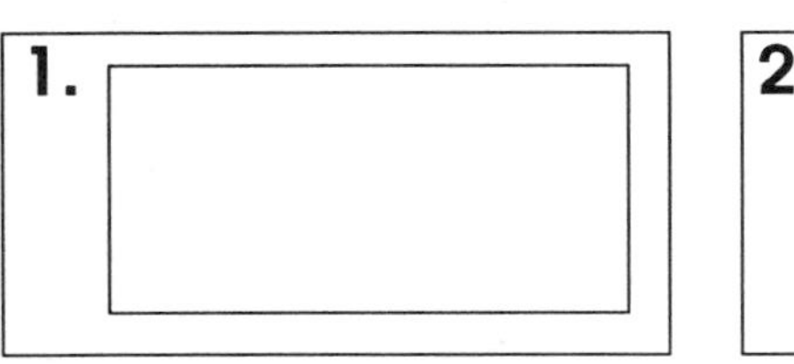

1. Use a rectangular piece of paper.

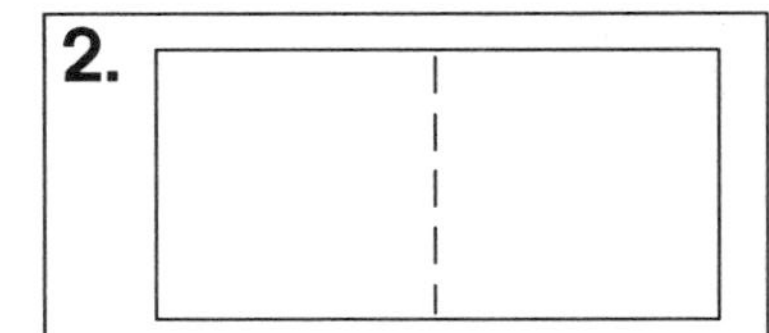

2. Fold it in half.

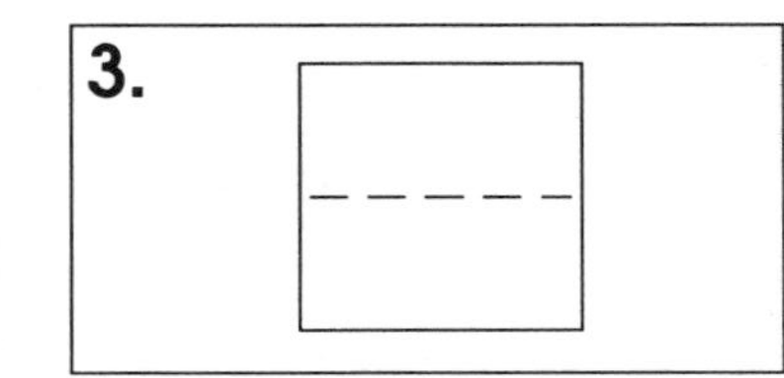

3. Fold in half again, top to bottom.

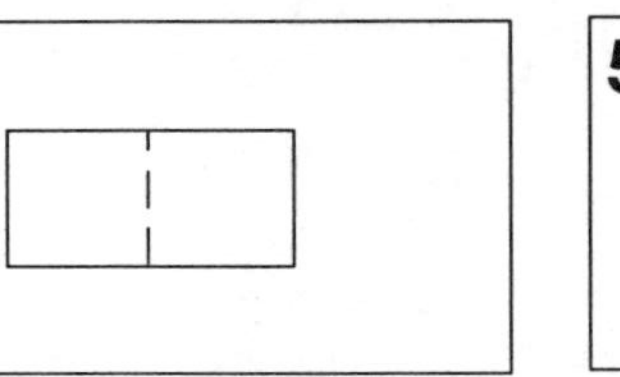
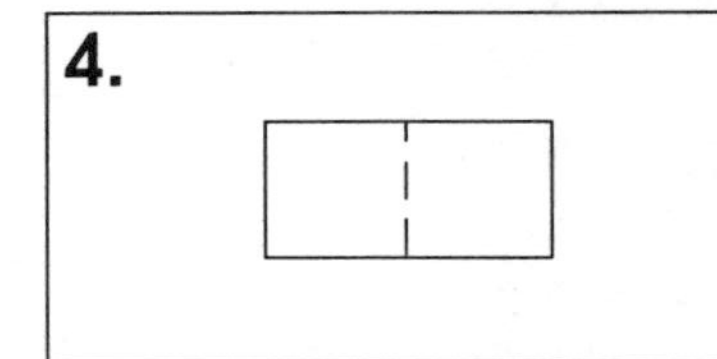

4. Fold again.

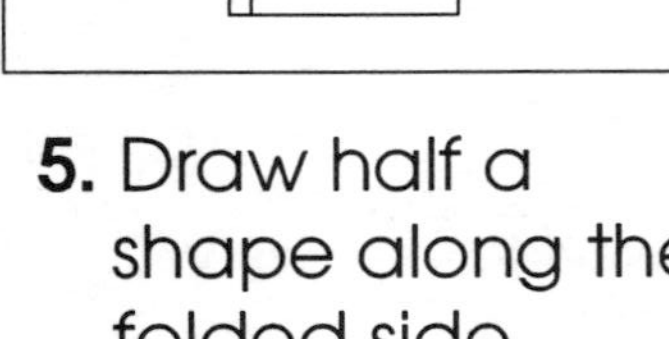
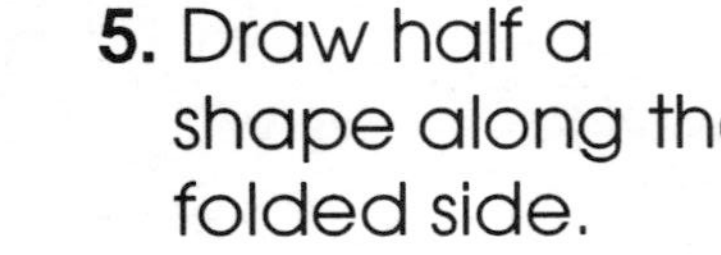

5. Draw half a shape along the folded side.

6. Cut out shape.

7. Staple along straight side.

8. Bend each piece into a 3-D model.

9. Decorate and hang on tree.

10. Variations: bell, star, angel, heart.

More paper fun:

Paper chains

1. Cut long pieces of coloured paper strips.
2. Loop and staple together.
3. Hang to decorate tree and rooms.

Paper doilies

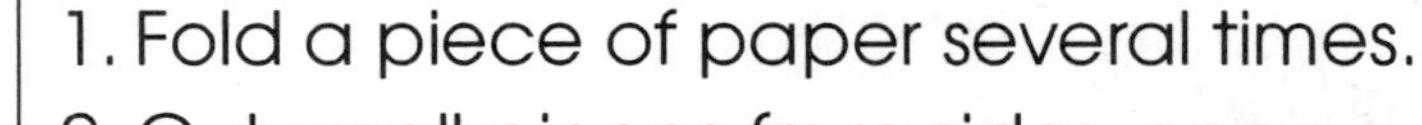
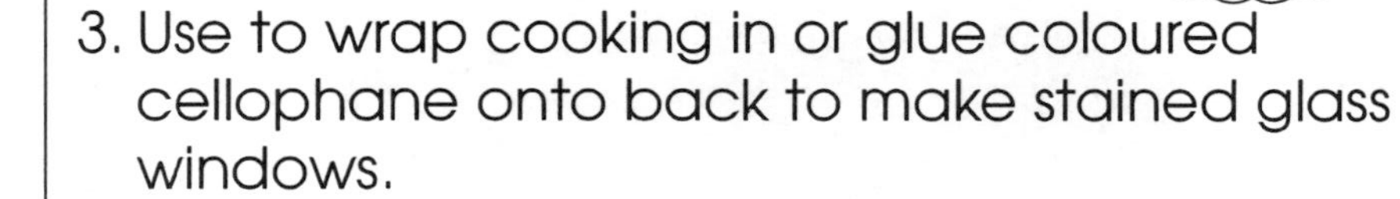

1. Fold a piece of paper several times.
2. Cut small pieces from sides, open out and decorate.
3. Use to wrap cooking in or glue coloured cellophane onto back to make stained glass windows.

Decorations

Name, colour and cut these decorations to hang on your tree.

Instructions on page 27 and 28 teacher resources

Christmas Templates

Tree

Gift Cube

cut

bend

Instructions on page 27 teacher resource

Nativity Characters

The Story of Christmas

Cut, staple in order and draw a picture for each.

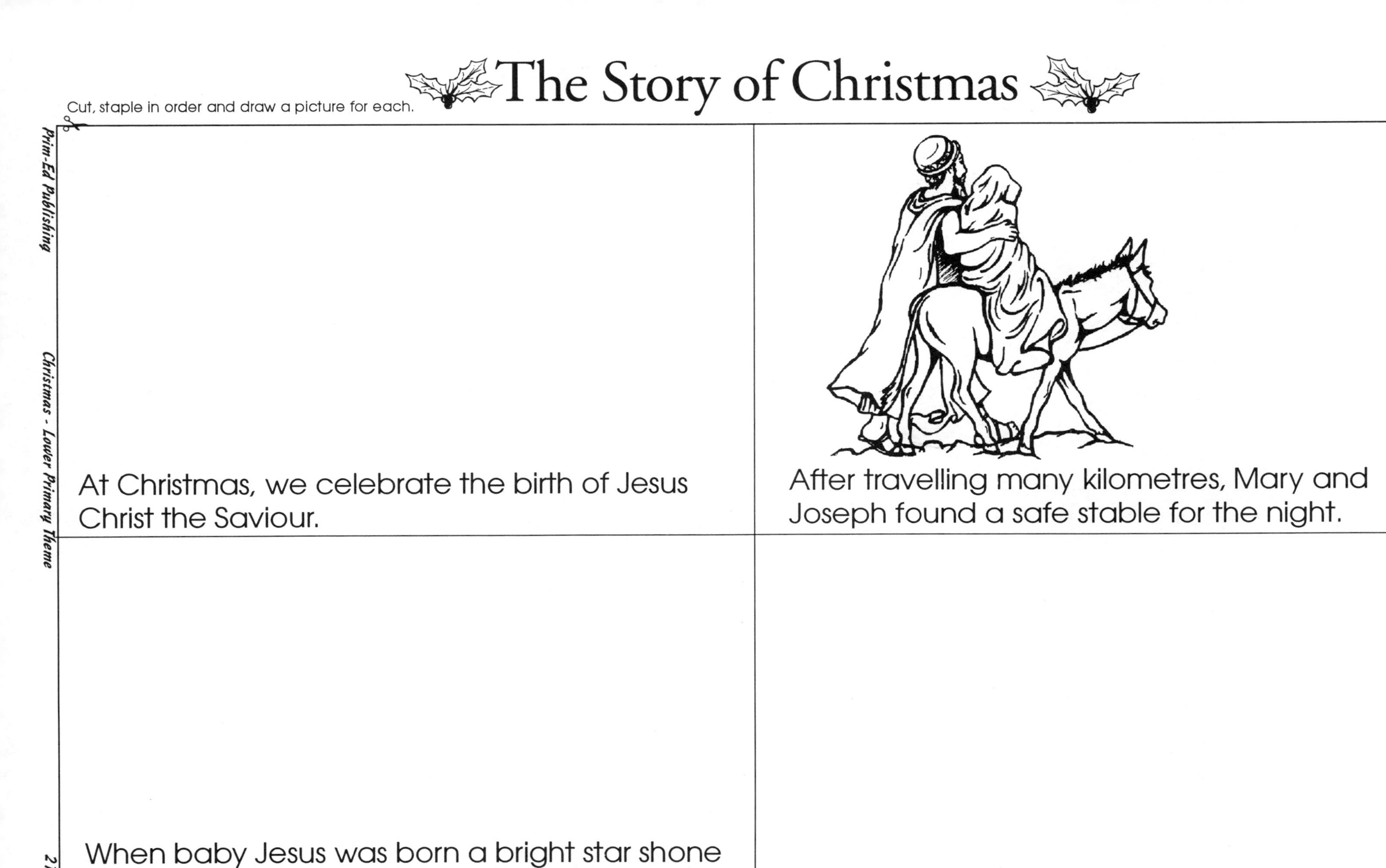

At Christmas, we celebrate the birth of Jesus Christ the Saviour.

After travelling many kilometres, Mary and Joseph found a safe stable for the night.

When baby Jesus was born a bright star shone in the sky. This led the wise men and shepherds to the stable.

They brought many gifts to celebrate the birth of this special baby boy.

Christmas Quiz

C_______________

Do_______________

Bl_______________

P_______________

R_______________

Cu_______________

Dan_______________

V_______________

Das_______________

Name Santa's nine reindeer.

Complete these Christmas song titles.

Deck the halls with ______________________________.

Rudolph the ______________________________.

Good King ______________________________.

All I want for Christmas is ______________________________.

Tick the correct box.

From what were Frosty the Snowman's eyes made?

- ☐ carrots
- ☐ sticks
- ☐ buttons

What was given on the first day of Christmas?

- ☐ a turtle dove
- ☐ a partridge in a pear tree
- ☐ three hens a laying

Father Christmas

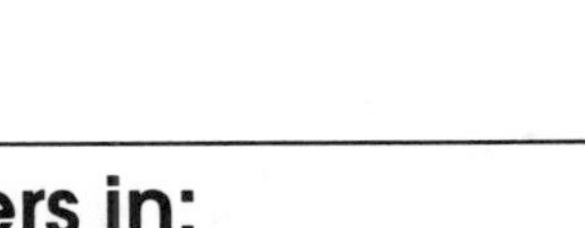

Father Christmas is known throughout the world as the giver of gifts. Many different countries have their own gift givers, such as Le Petit Noël in France, La Befana in Italy, Sinter Klaas in Holland and Baboushka in Russia.

All through the year, Father Christmas works with his elves at the North Pole preparing the Christmas toys.

On Christmas Eve, he visits children to bring them gifts. He travels from the cold of the North Pole and that is why he dresses in a warm red suit and hat, trimmed with white fur. He also wears heavy black boots to help grip the snow and protect his feet from the cold.

His sleigh, filled with sacks of toys, is pulled by reindeer. Rudolph leads the team because of his bright red nose.

When children wake on Christmas morning, they sometimes find gifts of food or toys left in their stockings by Father Christmas.

Name the gift givers in:

France ____________________

Russia ____________________

Italy ____________________

Draw and list some of the clothing Father Christmas wears.

____

____

____

____

____

____

____

My Favourite Christmas Dinner

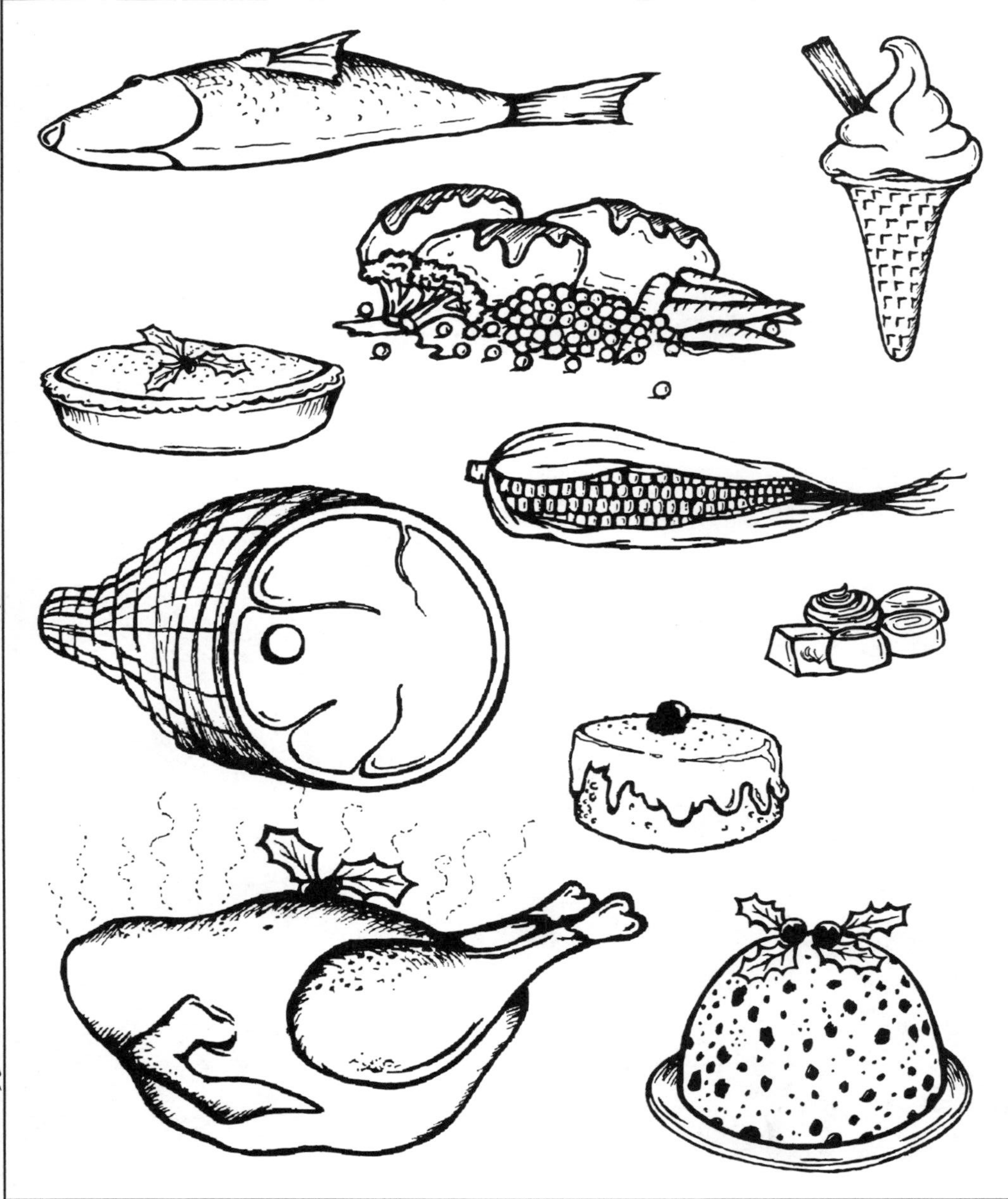

Use the pictures to list foods from your favourite Christmas dinner.

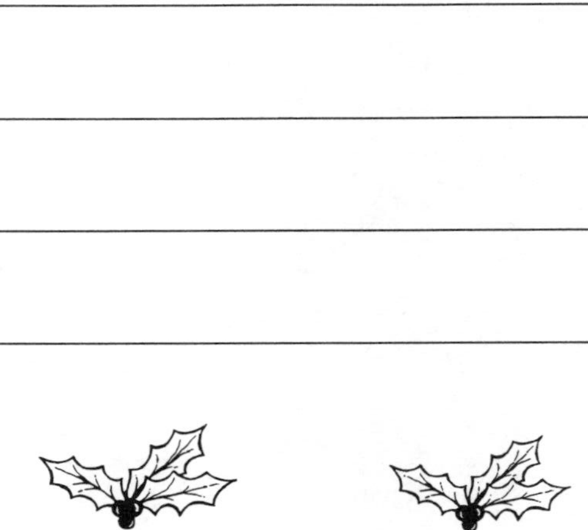

Colour, cut and glue your favourite food pictures onto a paper plate. Staple your list to the bottom of the plate.

Lights, Candles, Crackers and Safety

Lights and crackers are sometimes unsafe.
Read and complete these rules.

These words may help you to complete the rules.

hot swallow choke electrocute

1. Be careful of cords and power points because

____

____

2. Keep babies away from the small toys because

____

____

3. Keep eyes away from crackers and candles because

____

____

Decorate this cracker with a colourful pattern.

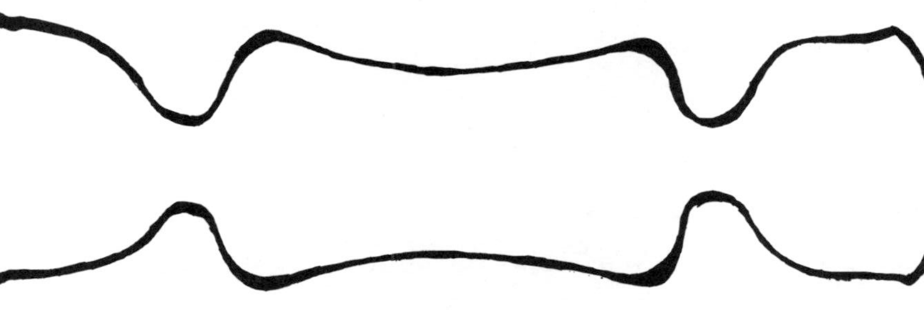

Make your own safe crackers.

You will need:
a cardboard roll
wrapping paper
small toys, balloons or lollies
ribbon for tying ends

Write two rules about safety with candles, crackers, lights or decorations on the tree.

1. ______________________________

____

2. ______________________________

____

Teacher resource

Read about these special customs.

- yule log
- carol singing
- bonbons
- festivals
- giving gifts
- coins in the pudding

Christmas gift tags

Enlarge to write Christmas greetings or decorations.

	To: From:	Merry Christmas
	Christmas Greetings from:	
	Merry Christmas	
Christmas Greetings from:		To: From:

Christmas recipe

Santa Surprises

You will need:

120 g margarine
pinch of salt
1 cup plain flour
1 tablespoon milk
milk for glazing
icing for decorating
1/2 cup icing sugar
1 teaspoon vanilla
1 cup self-raising flour
1 egg yolk
chocolate chips
red food colouring

1. Combine margarine, icing sugar and salt until creamy, then stir in vanilla and egg yolk.
2. Sift flours into mixture, add milk and mix to a firm dough.
3. Cover and refrigerate for 30 minutes.
4. Roll out onto a floured board and cut into circle shapes.
5. Decorate with chocolate chips for eyes. Beard and hat can be cut from left-over dough.
6. Press dough firmly and glaze with milk.
7. Cook on a greased tray for 15 minutes or until golden.
8. When cool, decorate with icing and lollies.

Felt finger puppets

1. Cut out felt finger puppet designs.
2. Add buttons and felt pieces.
3. Act out nativity scene or Christmas play, or hang from tree or presents.

Teacher resource

Answers

Page 13 - Red Elf makes cars, Yellow Elf makes rabbits, Green Elf makes necklaces, Orange Elf makes trains, Blue Elf makes teddies, Brown Elf makes bride dolls.
Page 22 - Rudolph, Dancer, Prancer, Vixen, Dasher, Comet, Cupid, Donner and Blitzen.
Boughs of holly, red-nosed reindeer, Wenceslas, my two front teeth.
Buttons, a partridge in a pear tree.

Nativity scene
Cut out a large circle. Draw a line to the centre and cut. Twist into a cone shape and staple. Colour , cut out and glue nativity characters onto the cone shape. Decorate with scrap materials.

Variation:

Father Christmas
Paint red and white and decorate with cottonwool.

Angel
Twist into a cone shape and cut half circle for wings.

Christmas trees

Instructions

Easy-fit trees
(template on page 19)
Enlarge and copy onto thick coloured card.
Cut templates for tree shapes.
Cut through centre lines and fit together.

Natural trees
Plant a dead branch from a tree into a bucket.
Spray pine cones, nuts and leaves with green, red and gold paint and decorate.

Cone tree
Cut out a large circle.
Cut a line from the outside into the centre.
Twist around to form a cone shape, staple and decorate with colourful paper chains.

Hand tree
Trace hand several times onto green or brown paper.
Cut out and glue to make a tree.
Variation - use class hands to make a giant Christmas tree.

Popcorn tree
Colour popcorn with green food colouring. Draw a tree shape onto card and glue popcorn to outline tree shape.
or
Thread cooked popcorn onto long pieces of cotton and hang on tree. A terrific tree decoration and edible too!

Teacher resource

Candles
Equipment:
- different size and colour candles
- eggtimer or clock
- large sheets of brown or coloured paper
- glue, seeds, felt, macaroni and ribbons
- potato peeler
- glitter or tinsel

Candle experiments

Burning candles (see page 14)
1. Time the burning of different size candles.
2. Record the size before lighting and measure at regular intervals.
3. Place candles near a draft or in a cupboard to observe burning rate.

Melting candles
Melt down different coloured candles and make new candles using different coloured wax.

Christmas Wreath
Instructions:
1. Cut a large, thick cardboard ring.
2. Cut, colour and decorate with Christmas pictures, wrapping paper and ribbons.
3. Add natural objects such as nuts, pine cones and red and gold painted leaves.
4. Hang on door knob.

Variations:
Use a wire coat-hanger bent into a circular shape. Cook and varnish dough decorations to be tied onto the wire.

Christmas Gift Cubes
(Template on page 19)

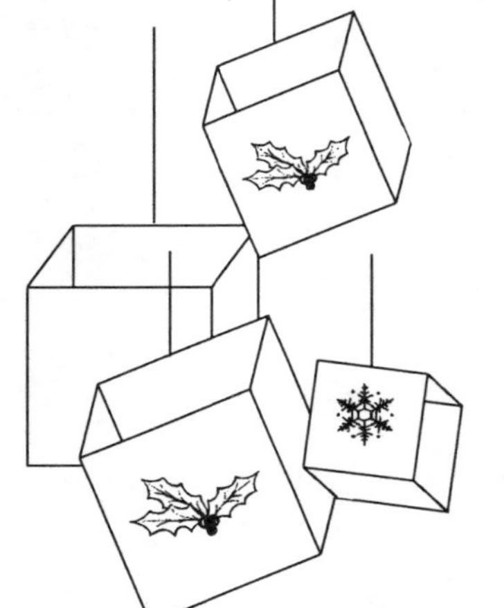

Equipment:
- scissors
- sticky tape
- string
- coloured pencils, or felt pens
- glue
- scrap coloured paper or ribbon

Instructions:
1. Enlarge template and copy onto stiff coloured card.
2. Cut along solid lines and fold along dotted lines.
3. Tape edges together.
4. Attach string to hang on tree.